In the Woods,

In the Meadow,

In the Sky

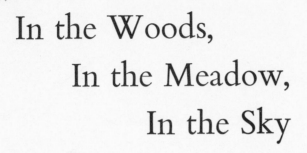

In the Woods,
In the Meadow,
In the Sky

BY AILEEN FISHER

Illustrated by Margot Tomes

Charles Scribner's Sons · *New York*

Contents

In the Woods

Pussy Willows

Close your eyes
and do not peek
and I'll rub Spring
across your cheek—
smooth as satin,
soft and sleek—
close your eyes
and do not peek.

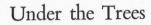

Under the Trees

We scuffed through the woods
and didn't see anything,
anything big or small,

Didn't see a swallow
or a cottontail to follow
or a scamper or a whisk at all.

We *sat* in the woods
as quiet as anything,
quiet and tucked away,

And out came a rabbit
in his hoppy sort of habit,
and a chipmunk,
           and a robin,
                and a jay.

A Whistle

I wouldn't want a whistle
from a weeping willow,
I wouldn't want a whistle
that was feeling sad.
I'd rather have a whistle
from a twinkly aspen,
so everything I whistled
would be glad, glad, glad.

Bluebird

In the woods a piece of sky
fell down, a piece of blue.
"It must have come from very high,"
I said. "It looks so new."

It landed on a leafy tree
and there it seemed to cling,
and when I squinted up to see,
I saw it had a *wing*,
and then a *head*, and suddenly
I heard a bluebird sing!

Rain of Leaves

It's raining big,
it's raining small,
it's raining autumn leaves
in fall.

It's raining gold
and red and brown
as autumn leaves
come raining down.

It's raining everywhere
I look.
It's raining bookmarks
on my book!

Windy Tree

Think of the muscles
a tall tree grows
in its leg, in its foot,
in its wide-spread toes—
not to tip over
and fall on its nose
when a wild wind hustles
and tussles and blows.

Climbing

The trunk of a tree
is the road for me
on a sunny summer day.

Up the bark
that is brown and dark
through tunnels of leaves that sway
and tickle my knees
in the trembly breeze,
that's where I make my way.

Leaves in my face
and twigs in my hair
in a squeeze of a place,
but I don't care!

Some people talk
of a summer walk
through clover and weeds and hay.

Some people stride
where the hills are wide
and the rocks are speckled gray.

But the trunk of a tree
is the road for me
on a sunny summer day.

Hideout

They looked for me
and from my nook
inside the oak
I watched them look.

Through little slits
between the leaves
I saw their looking
legs and sleeves.

They would have looked
all over town
except—
I threw some acorns down.

Holes of Green

Trees are full of holes—
between the leaves, I mean.
But if you stand away enough
the holes fill up with green.

Aspen Leaves

In any kind of woodland,
in any kind of breeze,
aspens are the singingest
of any kind of trees.

In the Treetops

Wind plays in the treetops,
wind sways in the treetops,
wind stays in the treetops
up where it's green and high.

Wind springs through the treetops,
wind sings through the treetops,
wind swings through the treetops.
I wish that so could I!

Open House

If I were a tree
I'd want to see
a bird with a song
on a branch of me.

I'd want a quick
little squirrel to run
up and down
and around, for fun.

I'd want the cub
of a bear to call,
a porcupine, big,
and a tree-toad, small.

I'd want a katydid
out of sight
on one of my leaves
to sing at night.

And down by my roots
I'd want a mouse
with six little mouselings
in her house.

Autumn Leaves

One of the nicest beds I know
isn't a bed of soft white snow,
isn't a bed of cool green grass
after the noisy mowers pass,
isn't a bed of yellow hay
making me itch for half a day—
but autumn leaves in a pile *that* high,
deep, and smelling like fall, and dry.
That's the bed where I like to lie
and watch the flutters of fall go by.

Stay-at-Homes

Some birds leave
when it's Autumn Eve
and wind is like a comb—
raking the gold
the treetops hold—
but some birds never roam.

In spite of the snow
and stars that glow
in winter's frosty dome,
they tuck their heads
in their feather beds
and make themselves at home.

Snowball Wind

The wind was throwing snowballs.
It plucked them from the trees
and tossed them all around the woods
as boldly as you please.

I ducked beneath the spruces
which didn't help a speck;
the wind kept throwing snowballs
and threw one down my neck.

Beneath the Snowy Trees

When boughs of spruces bend with snow
to way below their knees,
little caves and caverns show
beneath the snowy trees—
caves so secret, caves so low,
I think it would be fun
to be a rabbit who could go
and look in every one.

In the Meadow

When Spring Appears

Meadowlarks
give lusty cheers
when spring appears,
when spring appears.

Buds and seeds
prick up their ears
and blades of grass
show eager spears.

And only *icicles*
weep tears
when spring appears,
when spring appears.

Meadow of Hay

In a meadow of hay
on a sun-bright day
on the grassy sun-streaked floor,
the meadow mice stay
and cottontails play
and my puppy and I explore.

In a meadow of hay
where the shadows sway
there's a wonderful place to lie,
with grass and clover
roofing us over
between the slits of sky.

Snail's Pace

Maybe it's so
that snails are slow.
They trudge along and tarry.

But isn't it true
you'd slow up, too,
if you had a house to carry?

Daddy Longlegs

Don't you think a daddy longlegs
has a lot of fun
using all those stilts to walk
and all those stilts to run?

When It Rains

When it rains,
when it rains,
the magpie complains,
the pathway
turns muddy and brown,
the horses look sad
but the meadow is glad
and puddles

      up
jump   and

        down.

Busy Summer

Bees
make wax and honey,

Spiders,
webs of silk.

Wasps
make paper houses.

Cows
make cream and milk.

Dandelions
make pollen
for the bees to take.

Wish that I
had something
I knew how to make.

Meadow Morning

Did you ever go early
to take a walk
where weeds wear earrings
on every stalk,
and grass is shiny
as glass, and dewy,
and wild red clover
is sweet and chewy?

Did you ever go early
to walk for fun
where birds and beetles
are on the run,
getting their shopping
and calling done
before it's too hot
in the summery sun?

Butterfly Tongues

We wouldn't need straws for bottles,
we wouldn't need straws to drink,
if we had tongues like butterflies
we'd never need straws, I think.

If we had tongues uncoiling
like tubes without a kink,
we could sip way down like butterflies
when we wanted a way-down drink.

The Frog's Lament

"I can't bite
like a dog,"
said the bright
green frog.

"I can't nip,
I can't squirt,
I can't grip,
I can't hurt.

"All I can do
is hop and hide
when enemies come
from far and wide.

"I can't scratch
like a cat.
I'm no match
for a rat.

"I can't stab,
I can't snare,
I can't grab,
I can't scare.

"All I can do
my whole life through
is hop," said the frog,
"and hide from view."

And that's
what I saw him
up and do.

Mouse Roads

I wonder if field mice
working away
on mouse roads running
through clover and hay
put up markers
that mice can read—
like Clover Walk Lane
and Do Not Speed,
School Zone, Caution!
Fleet Street, Main—
so they'll know how to go
in the dark and rain.

Who Scans the Meadow?

Who scans the meadow up and down
   from where his little niche is?

Who wears a coat of grayish brown
   with grayish brownish britches?

Who hurries, full of leaps and hops,
   across the fields and ditches?

Whose mouth is full of clover tops,
   whose nose is full of twitches?

About Caterpillars

What about caterpillars?
Where do they crawl
when the stars say, "Frost,"
and the trees say, "Fall?"

Some go to sleep
in a white silk case
when the winds say, "Blow!"
and the clouds say, "Race!"

Some sleep in bags
of woven brown
or curl in a ball
when the year says, "Frown."

None has the least
little urge to know
what the world is like
when the sky says, "Snow."

On a Windy Day

Down the meadow,
down the meadow,
I run barefoot through the hay,
green and yellow,
patched with shadow,
on a runny windy day.

Down the meadow,
down the meadow,
I run barefoot through a sea,
waves of yellow,
waves of shadow,
waves of green that tickle me.

On an Autumn Night

At the meadow's edge
where the pond is bright
frogs sink down
on an autumn night
under the mud
and out of sight
before the world
turns cold and white
and storm windows cover
the pond up tight.

Flowers at Night

Some flowers close their petals,
blue and red and bright,
and go to sleep all tucked away
inside themselves at night.

Some flowers leave their petals
like windows open wide
so they can watch the goings-on
of stars and things outside.

Buzzy Old Bees

There wouldn't be apples
on apple trees,
or daisies or clover
or such as these,
if it weren't for fuzzy old
buzzy old bees,
dusting pollen
from off their knees
on apple blossoms,
on apple trees,
and clover and daisies
and such as these.

In the Sky

The Sun

Every day coming,
every day going,
bringing a goldness
out of the black,

Every day climbing
over the heavens,
sinking at sunset,
soon to be back,

Coming and going,
going and coming,
leaving no footprint,
leaving no track.

After the Rain is Over

After the sky
is bright again,
after the rain is over,
it's easy to tell
where the wind has been—
smelling the wild sweet clover!
Smelling so hard
and smelling so well
the air is flooded
with clover smell.

Voice of the Sky

The sky has the oldest voice
that ever has been heard—
it sighs,
it roars,
it cries,
yet never speaks a word.

Over the hill it comes
through treetops autumn-thinned—
it sings,
it moans,
it hums.
Listen, the wind, the wind!

On the Wing

When the birds fly south
over hill and vale,
when the birds fly south
over sod and shale,
when the birds fly south
in a lively throng,
they take the last of summer along.

When the birds fly north
over town and plain,
when the birds fly north
over wood and lane,
when the birds fly north
with a burst of song,
they bring the first of the spring along.

Airlift

Over the meadow,
over the clover,
an airlift goes
till the day is over,
heavy with freight
when skies are sunny—
thousands of bees
are making honey!

Sky Net

I know a busy fisherman
who fishes where it's dry.

He spreads his net
where nothing's wet,
he spreads it in the sky.

He doesn't care to catch a fish
that likes to swim
and splash and swish,
he only has a spider-wish—
to catch a bug or fly.

Butterfly Wings

How would it be
on a day in June
to open your eyes
in a dark cocoon,

And soften one end
and crawl outside,
and find you had wings
to open wide,

And find you could fly
to a bush or tree
or float on the air
like a boat at sea . . .

How would it be?

Comma in the Sky

A comma hung above the park,
a shiny punctuation mark;
we saw it curving in the dark
the night the moon was new.

A period hung above the bay,
immense though it was far away;
we saw it at the end of day
the night the moon was full.

Clouds

Wonder where they come from?
Wonder where they go?
Wonder why they're sometimes high
and sometimes hanging low?
Wonder what they're made of,
and if they weigh a lot?
Wonder if the sky feels bare
up there
      when clouds are *not*?

Please to Have a Little Rain

Please to have a little rain,
    Mrs. Sky.
Lawns and gardens wait in vain,
    grass is dry.
Robins must have mud, you know,
    for a nest.
Plants need watering to grow,
    rain is best.
Bushes standing in a huddle
    need a drink.
And my boat should have a puddle,
    don't you think?

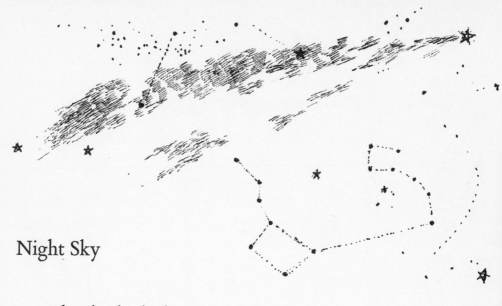

Night Sky

The sky looks bigger
by night than day,
with so many stars
so far away.

Old Man Moon

The moon is very, very old.
The reason why is clear—
he gets a birthday once a month,
instead of once a year.

Happy Birthday
to the Moon

Shooting Star

Wish upon a shooting star.
I watch.
I wait.
How few there are!

And then at last
a bright one flashes
down the sky
and turns to ashes
before I even
blink my lashes.

Wish upon a shooting star.
It comes so fast
from off so far
I can't think what
my wishes *are*
for wishing on
a shooting star.

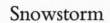

Snowstorm

The sky
kept falling, falling,
in fluffy bits of white.

The sky
kept spilling over
everywhere in sight.

I never knew
it was so big,
it fell all day and night.

The Kite

What do you see where you ride, kite,
close to the roof of the sky,
higher than swallows glide, kite,
higher than robins fly?
    What do you see?

How does it feel when you race, kite,
whisked by a current of air,
wind in your paper face, kite,
wind in your trailing hair?
    How does it feel?

Can you see how the river swirls, kite,
glinting its way along,
how the road through the hills uncurls, kite,
thin as a buckskin thong?
Take me along, along, kite,
    take me along!

Looking Through Space

If people are living
on Venus and Mars
and looking through space
at the planets and stars,
I wonder if Earth
seems a queer sort of thing,
with whiteness in winter
and greenness in spring.

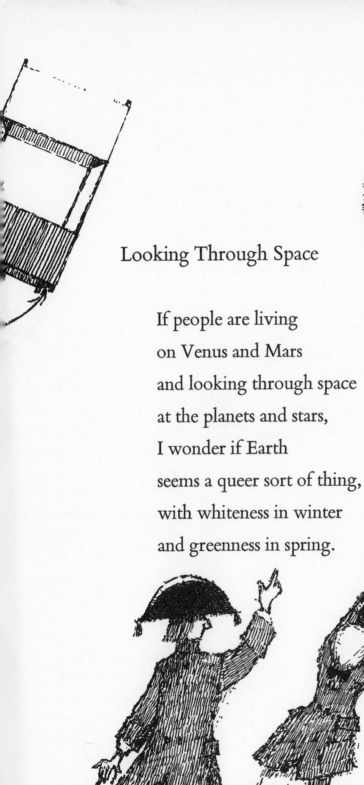

Index